武満 徹

ギターのための3つの小品

森のなかで

TORU TAKEMITSU
IN THE WOODS

Three pieces for guitar

SJ 1099

4

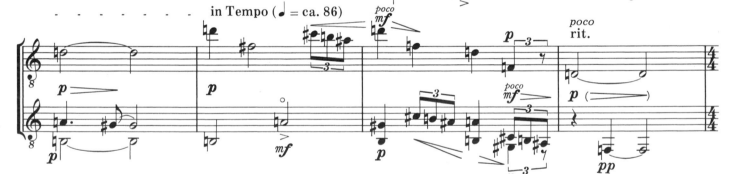

IN THE WOODS
森のなかで
Three pieces for guitar
ギターのための3つの小品

To John Williams

1. Wainscot Pond
ウェインスコット・ポンド
——after a painting by Cornelia Foss——
——コーネリア・フォスの絵画から——

Toru Takemitsu
武満 徹

独立した 3 つのギター曲からなる『森のなかで』は、1995年11月に作曲された。各曲は、以下のギタリストに献呈されている。

1. ウェインスコット・ポンド　―コーネリア・フォスの絵画から― ――ジョン・ウィリアムス

2. ローズデール――荘村清志

3. ミュアー・ウッズ――ジュリアン・ブリーム

第 1 曲目の《ウェインスコット・ポンド　―コーネリア・フォスの絵画から―》は、1996年 2 月29日、東京で行われた武満徹の告別式で佐藤紀雄により初演され、第 3 曲《ミュアー・ウッズ》は、10月 4 日、ロンドンで、ジュリアン・ブリームにより初演された。

第 2 曲《ローズデール》および全 3 曲の初演は、10月15日、東京で、荘村清志によって行われた。

演奏時間

1. 4分

2. 4分

3. 5.5分

IN THE WOODS was composed in November, 1995 and consists of three independent pieces. Each is dedicated to the following guitarists:

1. Wainscot Pond –after a painting by Cornelia Foss– ――to John Williams

2. Rosedale ――to Kiyoshi Shomura

3. Muir Woods ――to Julian Bream

The premiere of the first piece, *Wainscot Pond —after a painting by Cornelia Foss—*, took place on the occasion of the funeral service for Toru Takemitsu on February 29, 1996 in Tokyo performed by Norio Sato. The third piece, *Muir Woods*, was premiered by Julian Bream on October 4, 1996 in London. The work in its entirety as well as the second piece, *Rosedale*, was premiered by Kiyoshi Shomura on October 15, 1996 in Tokyo.

Duration of each piece:

1. 4 minutes

2. 4 minutes

3. 5.5 minutes

ABBREVIATION AND SYMBOL:

l.v. = Let vibrate

⊓ = Short fermata

5

2. Rosedale
ローズデール

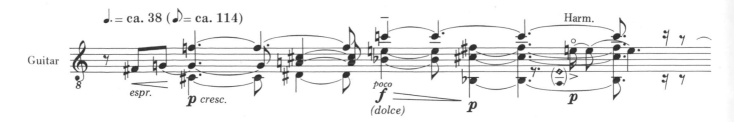

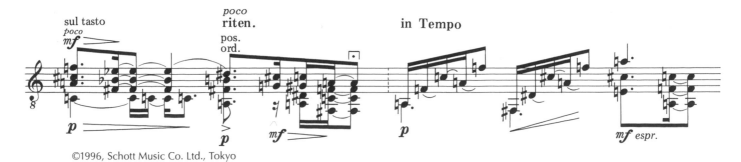

3. Muir Woods
ミュアー・ウッズ

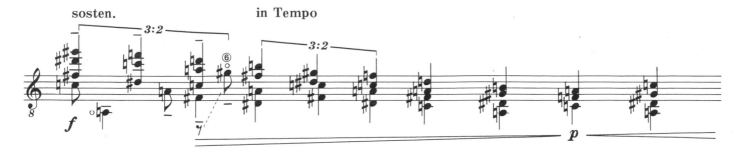

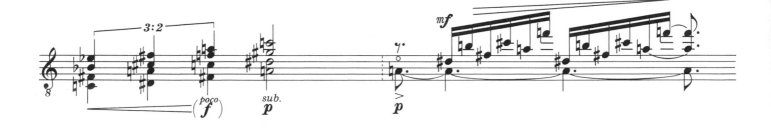

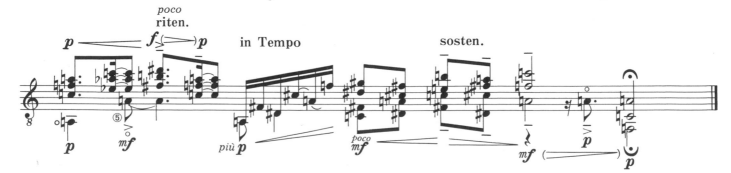

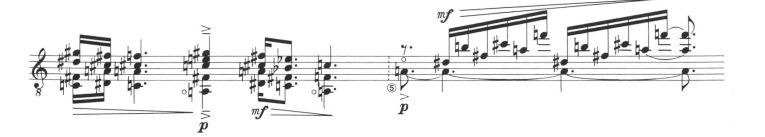

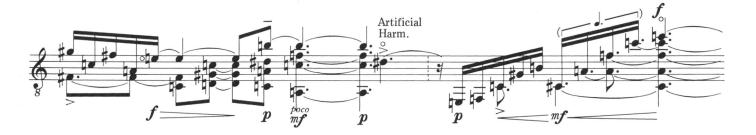

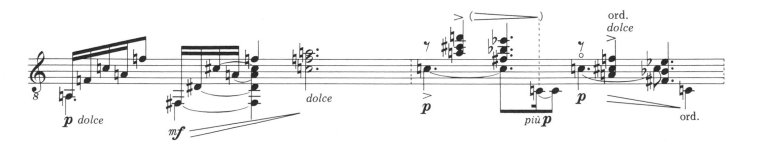

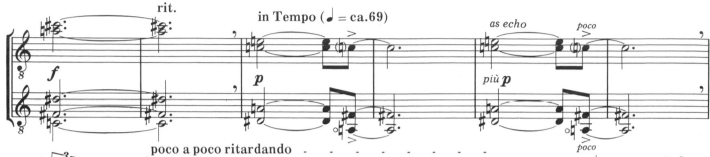

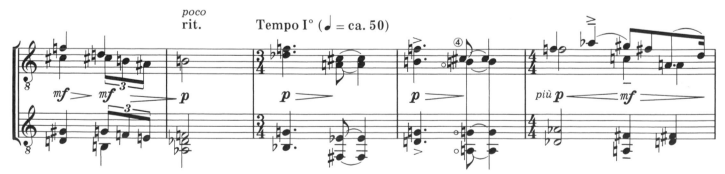

武満 徹《森のなかで》　　　　　　　　　　　●

ギターのための3つの小品

初版発行 ———————————————————————— 1996年10月15日
第1版第8刷⑧ ———————————————————————— 2021年8月25日
発行 ———————————————————————— ショット・ミュージック株式会社
————————————————————————— 東京都千代田区内神田1-10-1 平富ビル3階
————————————————————————— 〒101-0047
————————————————————————— (03)6695-2450
————————————————————————— www.schottjapan.com
————————————————————————— ISBN 978-4-89066-399-6
————————————————————————— ISMN M-65001-015-3